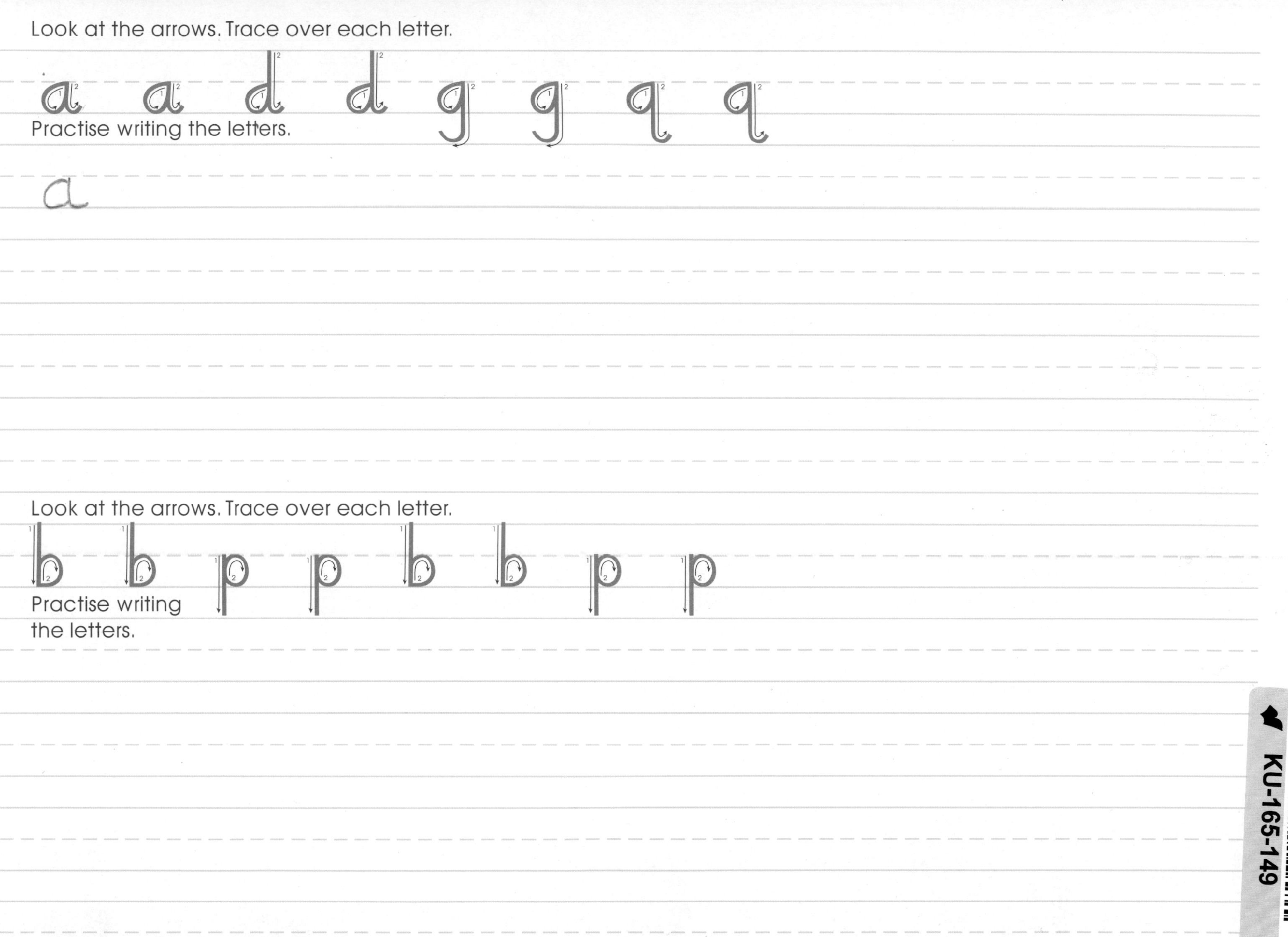

Look at the arrows. Trace over each letter.

Practise writing the letters.

Look at the arrows. Trace over each letter.

Practise writing the letters.

Look at the arrows. Trace over each letter.

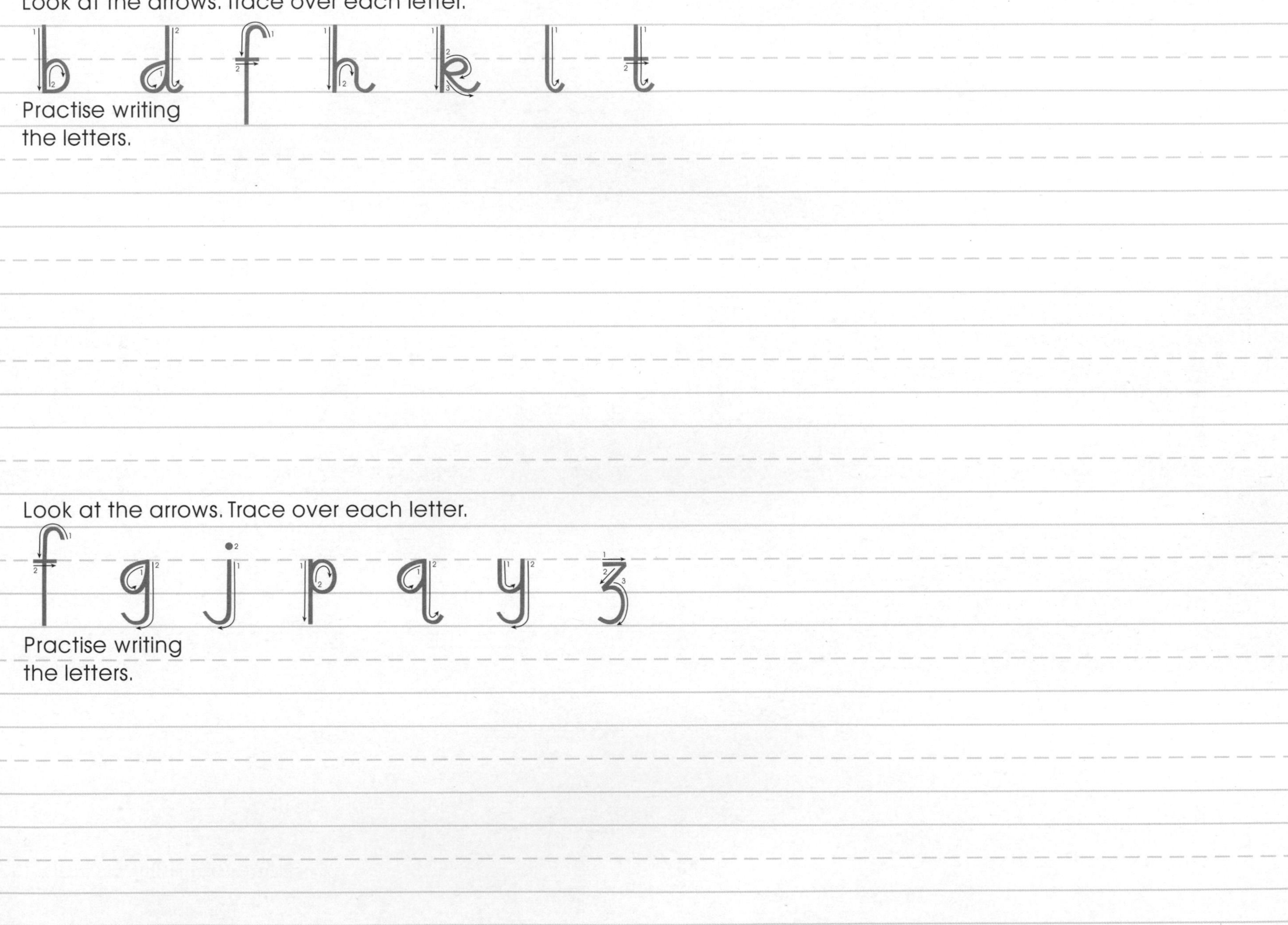

Look at the arrows. Trace over each letter.

m m n n r r

Practise writing the letters.

Look at the arrows. Trace over each letter.

u u v v w w

Practise writing the letters.

Look at the arrows. Trace over each letter.

s s c c o o e e

Practise writing the letters.

Look at the arrows. Trace over each number.

1 2 3 4 5 6 7 8 9 10

Practise writing the numbers.

Look at the arrows. Trace over each letter.

Aa Bb Cc Dd Ee

Ff Gg Hh Ii

Jj Kk Ll Mm Nn

Oo Pp Qq Rr

Ss Tt Uu Vv Ww

Xx Yy Zz

Look at the arrows. Trace over each letter.

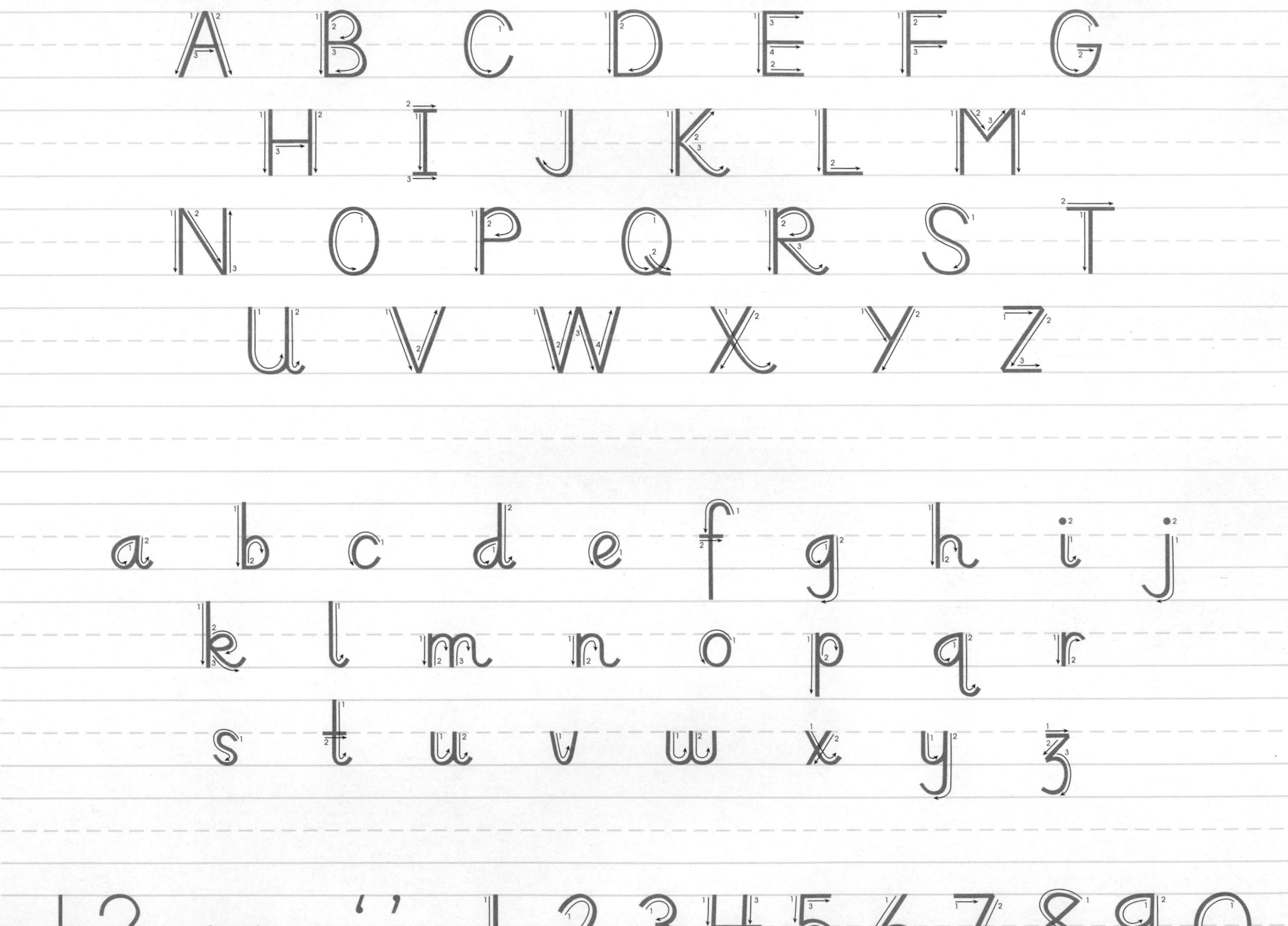

Practise writing the letter. Practise writing the sentence.

A A A

a a a

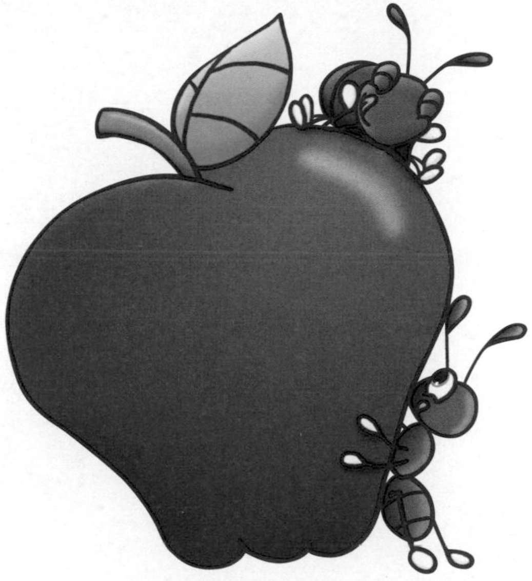

Annie Ant ate an apple.

Practise writing the letter. Practise writing the sentence.

B B B

b b b

Big Bob is a brown bear.

Practise writing the letter. Practise writing the sentence.

C C C

c c c

Cool Cat collects cookies.

Practise writing the letter. Practise writing the sentence.

D D D

d d d

Daring Dan dives deep.

Practise writing the letter. Practise writing the sentence.

E E E

e e e

Ed Elephant eats everything.

Practise writing the letter. Practise writing the sentence.

F F F

f f f

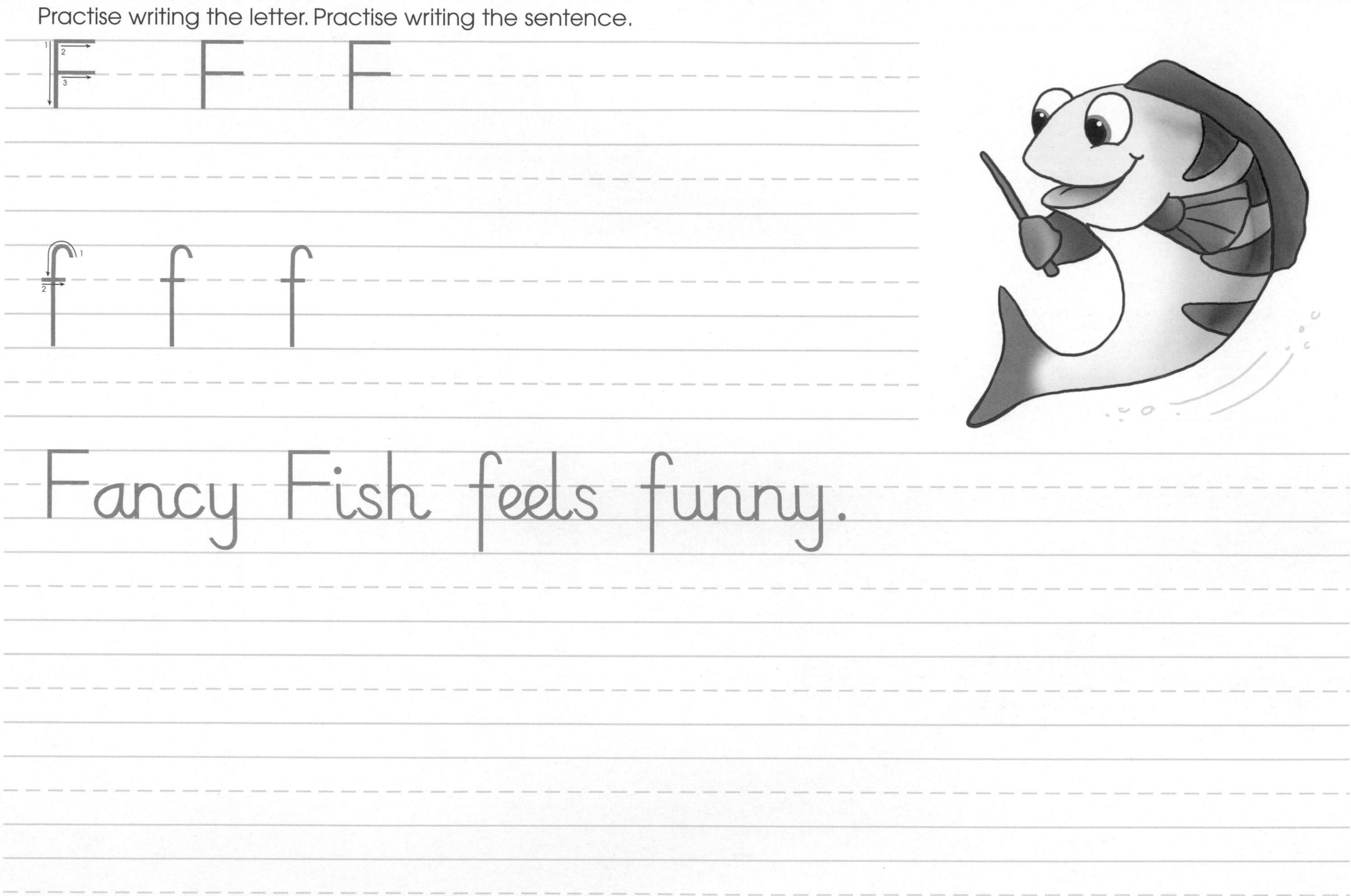

Fancy Fish feels funny.

Practise writing the letter. Practise writing the sentence.

G G G

g g g

Gail Goat likes green grass.

Practise writing the letter. Practise writing the sentence.

H H H

h h h

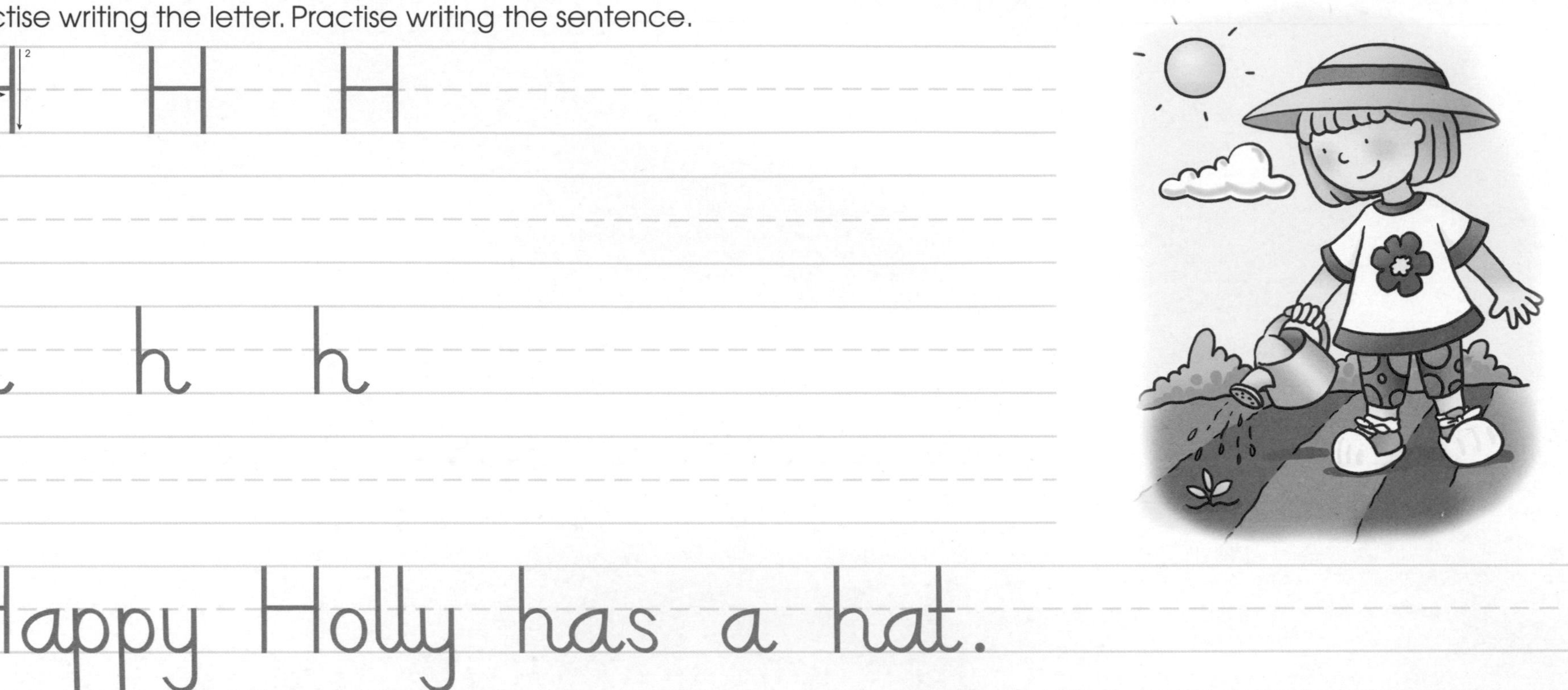

Happy Holly has a hat.

Practise writing the letter. Practise writing the sentence.

I I I

i i i

Impolite Iris is in the ice-cream.

Practise writing the letter. Practise writing the sentence.

J J J

j j j

Jolly Joe juggles jam jars.

Practise writing the letter. Practise writing the sentence.

K K K

k k k

Kim Kangaroo kept the kites.

Practise writing the letter. Practise writing the sentence.

L L L

l l l

Larry Lion loves leaves.

Practise writing the letter. Practise writing the sentence.

M M M

m m m

Mighty Monkey moves the moon.

Practise writing the letter. Practise writing the sentence.

N N N

n n n

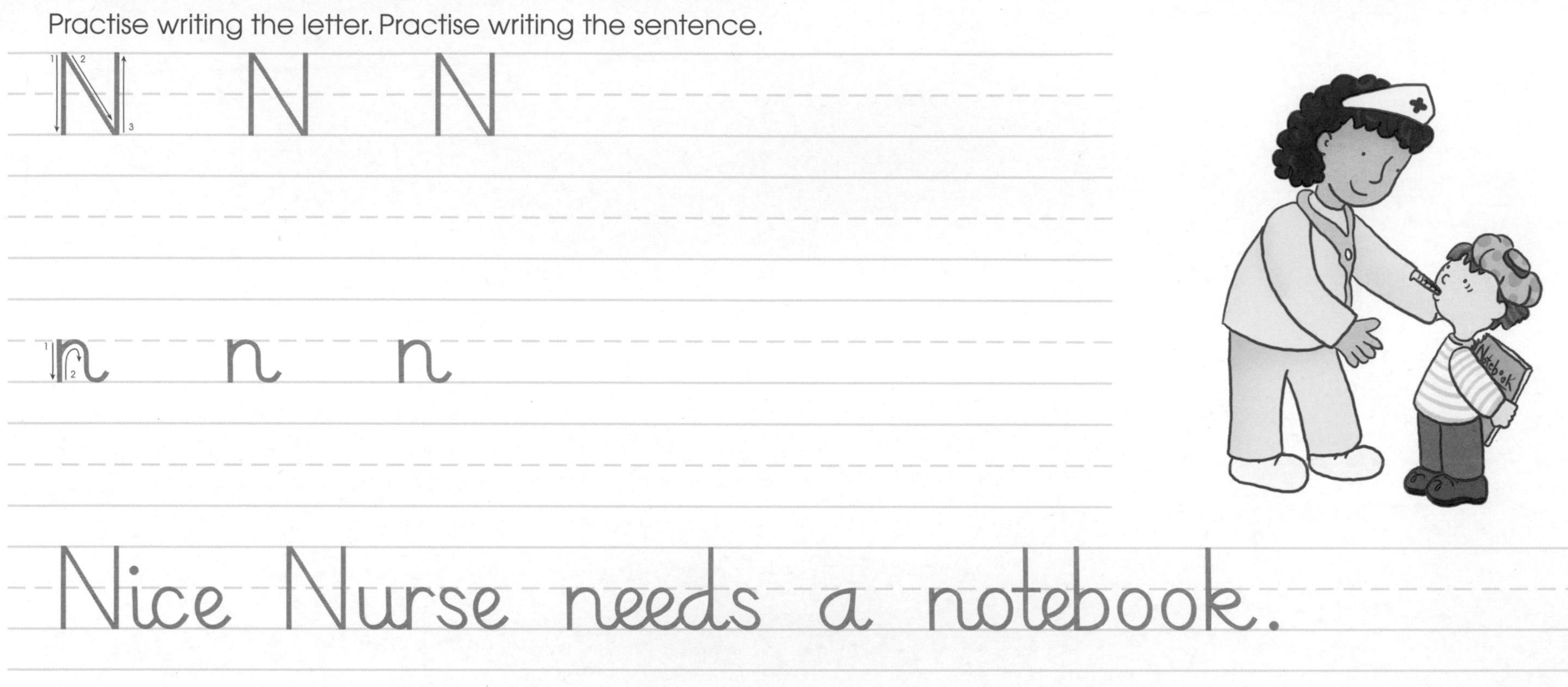

Nice Nurse needs a notebook.

Practise writing the letter. Practise writing the sentence.

O O O

o o o

Ollie Octopus occupies the ocean.

Practise writing the letter. Practise writing the sentence.

P P P

p p p

Pink Pig plays the piano.

Practise writing the letter. Practise writing the sentence.

Q Q Q

q q q

Quiet Queen quit quilting.

Practise writing the letter. Practise writing the sentence.

R R R

r r r

Rowdy Raccoon rocks the railcar.

Practise writing the letter. Practise writing the sentence.

S S S

s s s

Silly Seal swims to school.

Practise writing the letter. Practise writing the sentence.

T T T

t t t

Tom Turkey talks to two turtles.

Practise writing the letter. Practise writing the sentence.

U U U

u u u

Uppity Umpire uses an umbrella.

Practise writing the letter. Practise writing the sentence.

V V V

v v v

Vera Violet has a violet vase.

Practise writing the letter. Practise writing the sentence.

W W W

w w w

Weary Walrus wants a wheel.

Practise writing the letter. Practise writing the sentence.

X X X

x x x

Xavier X. had an extra x-ray.

Practise writing the letter. Practise writing the sentence.

Y Y Y

y y y

Yvette Yak yearns for a yo-yo.

Practise writing the letter. Practise writing the sentence.

Z Z Z

z z z

Zany Zebra zigzags to the zoo.

A Authors

Write the name of the author for each book title.

Milne, A.A.	Twain, Mark	Potter, Beatrix	Seuss, Dr	White, E.B.

1. The Adventures of Tom Sawyer

2. The Tale of Peter Rabbit

3. Winnie-the-Pooh

4. The Cat in the Hat

5. Charlotte's Web

B Buildings

Write the name of the building that matches each clue.

library	school	hospital	museum	hotel

1. where you go to be treated for health problems

2. a place that displays objects of permanent value

3. where learning takes place

4. where books may be borrowed or read

5. a building that provides lodging

C Countries

Write the name of the country that matches each clue.

Australia	Spain	China	France	England

1. you can visit the Eiffel Tower here

2. you can walk along a great wall here

3. you might see a koala here

4. you might eat paella here

5. London is the capital city

D Dogs

Write the name of the dog that matches each clue.

husky   boxer   greyhound   pointer   beagle

1. not a bus

2. points the way

3. rabbit chaser

4. does not wear gloves

5. looks like a wolf

E Ecosystems

Write the answer that completes each sentence.

ecology	habitat	oxygen	meteorology	botany

1. The environment in which a species lives is its ______ .

2. ______ is the study of how plants and animals interact.

3. The study of plants is called ______ .

4. ______ is the science of weather.

5. Plants and animals need water and ______ to live.

F Farm Animals

Write the name of the animal that matches each clue.

sheep	horse	cow	chicken	pig

1. raised on a dairy farm

2. raised for meat on a hog farm

3. raised now mainly for riding

4. raised for both food and clothing

5. raised for meat and eggs

G Board Games

Write the name of the board game that matches each clue.

Trivial Pursuit	Chess	Monopoly	Cluedo	Scrabble

1. uses play money to buy and sell property

2. a game of many questions

3. a strategy game played to capture the opponent's king

4. a word game that requires spelling and vocabulary

5. a 'whodunnit' board game

H Habitats

Write the habitat that matches each clue.

desert	oceans	swamps	rainforests	grasslands

1. a very dry place, not all are hot

2. wide areas covered with grasses and trees

3. hot and humid parts of the world

4. a home to fish and mammals

5. wetlands that are flooded all the time

I Insects

Write the name of the insect that matches each clue.

ladybird	firefly	mosquito	termite	ant

1. terminator

2. picnic pest

3. vampire insect

4. pyromaniac

5. female bug

J Jokes

Write the answer that makes the joke funny.

Palm   She wanted rich soil.   It gets unhoppy.   A bedbug.   Three days old.

1. What is an insect after it is two days old?

2. What happens when a frog gets stuck in the mud?

3. Why did the gardener bury her money?

4. Which trees clap?

5. What kind of insect sleeps most?

K Know Your Bones

Label the bones with the correct word.

skull	kneecap	ankle	shin	collarbone	elbow	jaw	pelvis

L Logic Puzzles

Patti, Mary and Paul each has a different favourite food.
Which is it, chicken, pizza or spaghetti?
Read the information in the charts below to complete the puzzle.
Write each child's favourite food on the line.

Patti ______________________________

Mary ______________________________

Paul ______________________________

Patti does not like chicken or pizza.

	Patti	Mary	Paul
Pizza	**no**		
Spaghetti	**yes**		
Chicken	**no**		

Mary will not eat foods that have tomatoes in them. (Hint: If Mary does not like foods with tomato, then she must like chicken.)

	Patti	Mary	Paul
Pizza	**no**	**no**	
Spaghetti	**yes**	**no**	
Chicken	**no**	**yes**	

Paul likes a food that starts with the same letter as his name. (Hint: If Paul likes pizza, then spaghetti or chicken must not be his favourite.)

	Patti	Mary	Paul
Pizza	**no**	**no**	**yes**
Spaghetti	**yes**	**no**	**no**
Chicken	**no**	**yes**	**no**

M Mammals

Write the name of the animal that matches each clue.

whale	elephant	bat	fox	giraffe

1. the longest neck

2. carries a trunk

3. the blue one is the largest mammal

4. flying mammal

5. known as sly

N Numbers Quiz

Solve the problems. Write the answers in the puzzle.

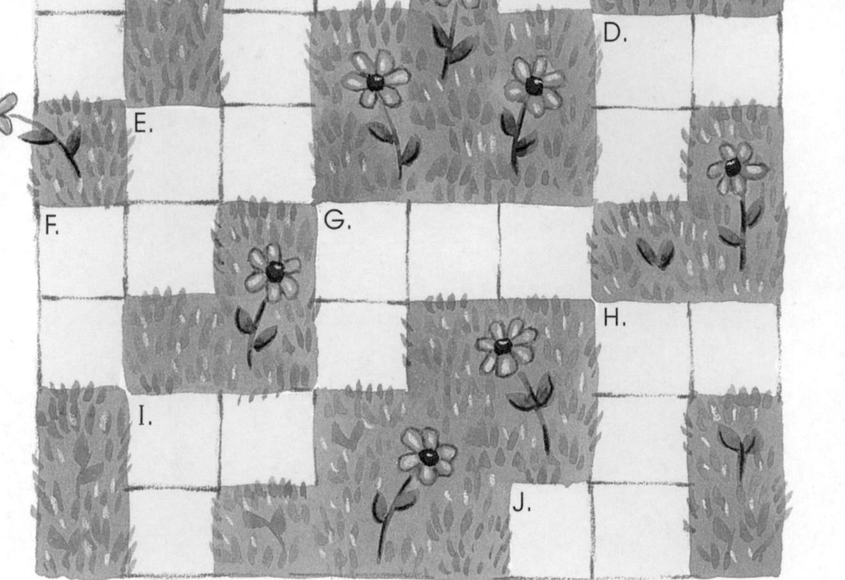

Across

A. 12 more than 10

B. 90, 95, 100, ____

C. 14 + 15 = ____

D. 8 + 9 = ____

E. 19 – 7 = ____

F. 3, 6, 9, ____

G. 120 – 15 = ____

H. 2 tens, 8 ones

I. 50p + 35p = ____

J. 29 – 13 = ____

Down

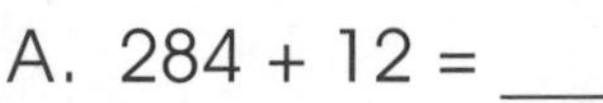
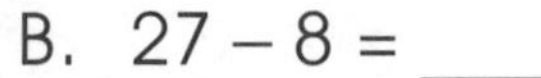

A. 284 + 12 = ____

B. 27 – 8 = ____

C. 2 hundreds, 2 tens, 2 ones

D. 5, 10, ____

E. one dozen

F. 2 x 9 = ____

G. 3 x 5 = ____

H. 2 hundreds, 3 tens, 6 ones

I. £1.00 – 15p = ____

O Oceans

Write on the lines to show where each ocean is located.

Atlantic Ocean   Indian Ocean   Pacific Ocean   Arctic Ocean   Antarctic Ocean

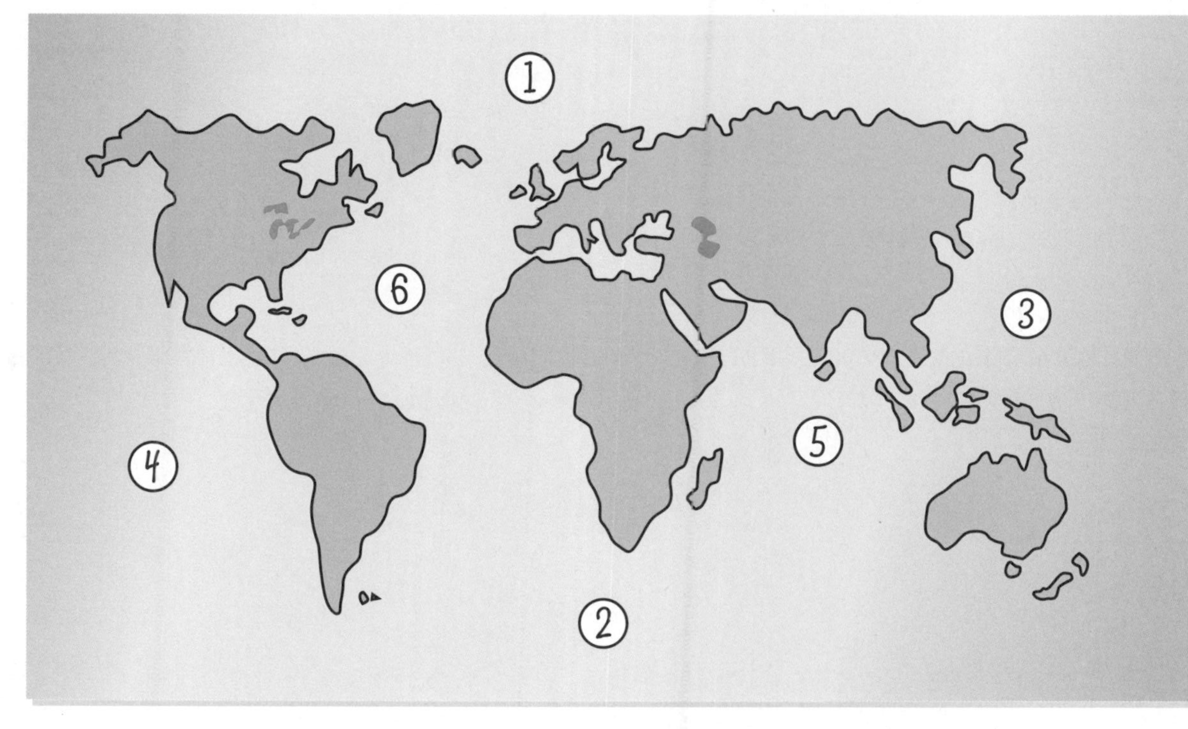

1.

2.

3.

4.

5.

6.

P People

Write the name of the person who matches each clue.

Dalai Lama	Nelson Mandela	Martin Luther King	Mother Teresa	Mahatma Gandhi

1. His philosophy of non-violence has influenced movements for peaceful change in India and the rest of the world.

2. An internationally renowned nun and founder of the Missionaries of Charity whose work among the poor of Calcutta was widely reported.

3. Before becoming President of South Africa, he was one of its chief anti-apartheid activists and an anti-apartheid saboteur.

4. An African American civil rights activist and one of the most significant leaders in US history and in the modern history of non-violence.

5. The respected leader of Tibetan Buddhism.

Q *Simile Quiz*

The nouns in these similes are wrong. Write the correct noun on the line.

silk	nails	feather	bird	night

1. as light as a rock ______

2. as dark as silk ______

3. as hard as chalk ______

4. as free as a bone ______

5. as smooth as night ______

R Rivers

Write the name of the continent where the river is located.

North America	Africa	South America	Asia

1. Nile

2. Amazon

3. Yangtze

4. Mississippi

S Sun

Write the answer that completes each sentence.

energy	galaxy	light and heat	gas	Milky Way

1. ______ is another word for star system.

2. The sun shines because it gives out ______ and ______ .

3. A star is made of ______ and has no solid surface.

4. Our galaxy is named the ______ ______ .

5. Light and heat are forms of ______ .

T Analogy Test

Write the word that completes the analogy.

computer	author	pound	rug	brake

1. Grass is to ground as ______ is to floor.

2. Bat is to cricketer as ______ is to writer.

3. Scissor is to cut as hammer is to ______ .

4. Artist is to painting as ______ is to novel.

5. Engine is to go as ______ is to stop.

U Countries Beginning with U

Write the answer that matches each clue.

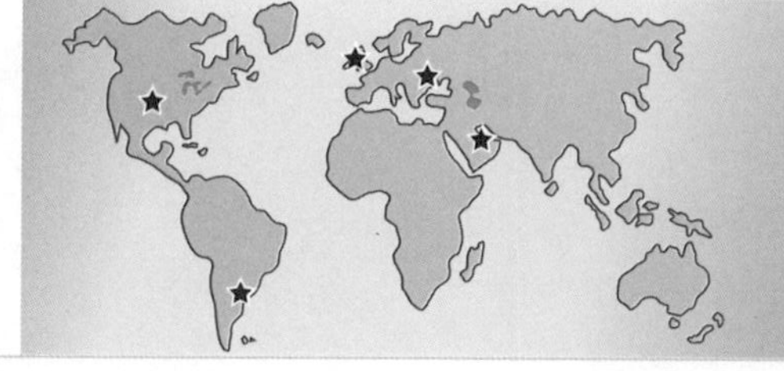

United Arab Emirates   Ukraine   United Kingdom   Uruguay   United States

1. Great Britain and Northern Ireland

2. a small country located in southern South America

3. a federal republic of 50 states located primarily in central North America

4. a part of the Middle East

5. a republic in eastern Europe

V Vegetables

Write the name of the vegetable in the matching plant part.

W Weather

Write the answer that matches each clue.

tornado	thunderstorm	hurricane	snowstorm	rainbow

1. My favourite dance is the twist.

2. I turn everything white.

3. I 'm one of the prettiest things that comes with rain.

4. I'm bigger and badder than a tornado.

5. When I rain, I pour, and pour some more.

X X Marks The Spot

Write the name of the city for each pair of coordinates.

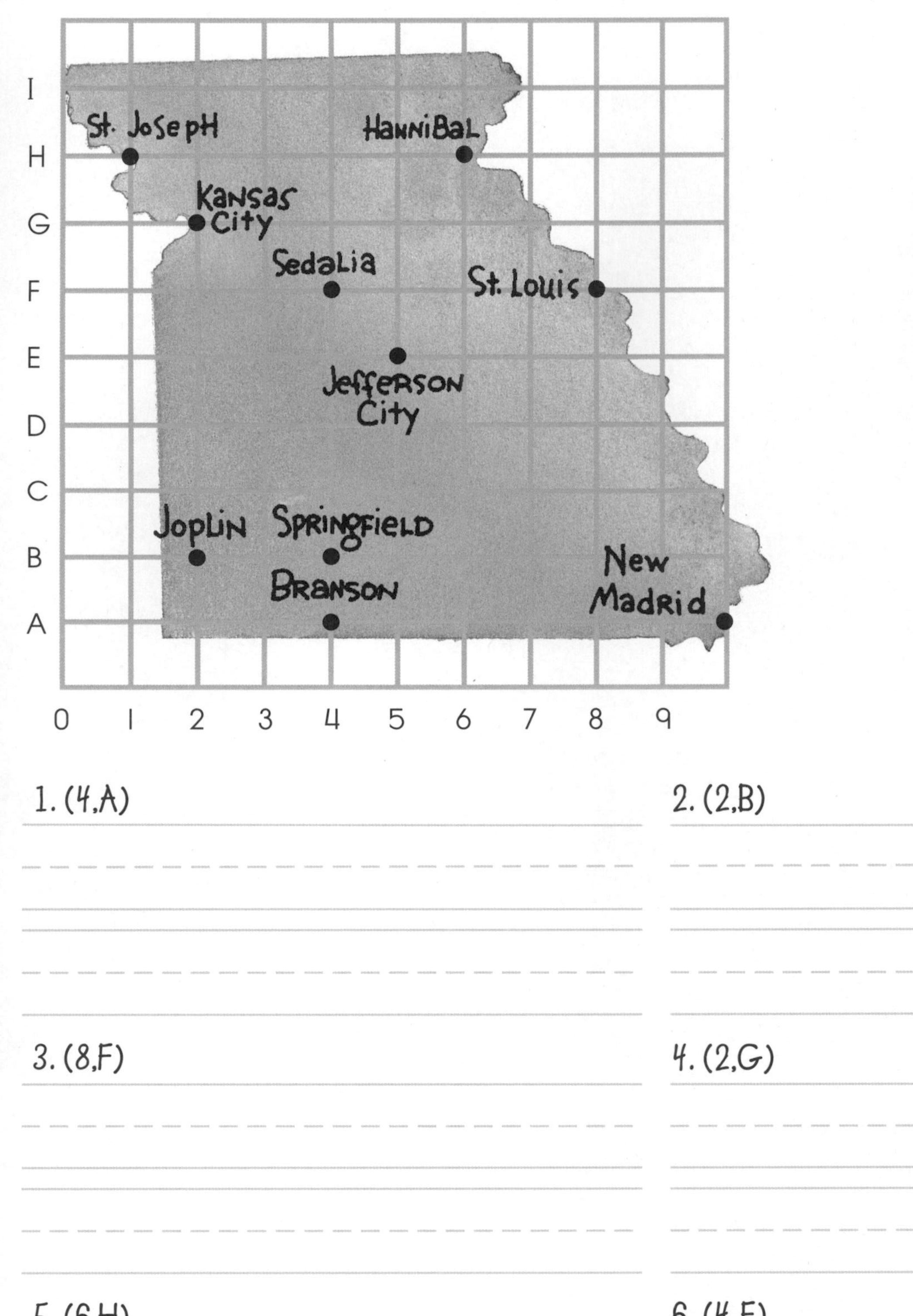

1. (4,A)

2. (2,B)

3. (8,F)

4. (2,G)

5. (6,H)

6. (4,F)

Y Yellowstone Park

Write the correct answer for each sentence.

Wyoming	glaciers	Louisiana Purchase	geyser	oldest

1. Yellowstone Park was shaped by volcanoes and ______ .

2. The Yellowstone region was acquired as part of the ______ ______ .

3. Yellowstone Park is located mainly in the US state of ______ .

4. Old Faithful is a famous ______ in the park.

5. The national park is the ______ in the world.

Z Zoo Quiz

Write the name of the animal that matches each clue.

platypus	flea	ostrich	cheetah	chameleon

1. I run up to 110 kilometres per hour.

2. I grow up to 2.5 metres tall and weigh 136 kilograms.

3. I can jump 130 times my own weight.

4. My tongue can be the length of my body.

5. I lay eggs instead of live young.

Water Words

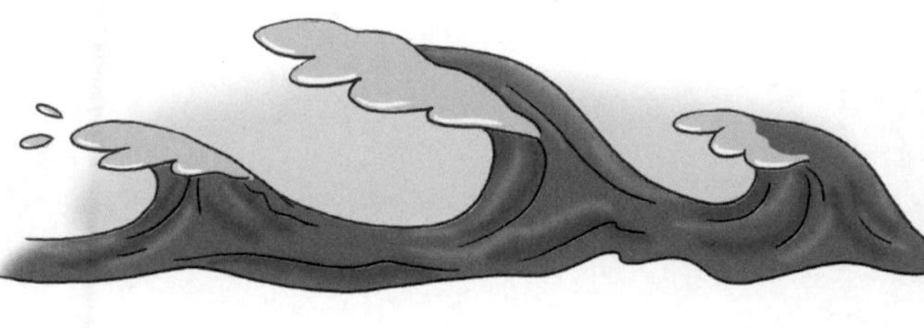

Write the word that matches the description.

tide	currents	salt	waves	sand

1. These are like giant rivers in the ocean. ________

2. something you can taste in the ocean water________

3. the daily rise and fall of ocean water caused by the sun and the moon________

4. These form when winds move ocean water toward the shore. ________

5. tiny pieces of rock and coral ________

Idioms

Idioms are expressions or phrases that do not mean what they say. Match each idiom with its meaning.

get angry	tell a secret	not understood	happy	be quiet

1. clear as mud ______

2. walking on air ______

3. bite your tongue ______

4. blow your top ______

5. spill the beans ______

Leaping Lizards

Write the word that completes each sentence.

tails	slugs	iguana	tongue	dinosaurs

1. Lizards lived during the time of the ______ .

2. A chameleon catches bugs with its long sticky ______ .

3. One lizard that eats plants is the ______ .

4. Some lizards eat ______ .

5. Some lizards drop their ______ when they're in trouble.

Weather Words

Write the word that completes each sentence.

wind	water	air pressure	precipitation	condensation

1. Rain, snow and hail are kinds of ______.

2. Drops of water on a cold can are ______ .

3. The push of air on the earth is ______ ______ .

4. Cold air can't hold as much ______ as warm air.

5. Moving air is ______.

Sports

Write the word that matches each clue.

tennis bowling squash golf football

1. love fifteen ______

2. small ball ______

3. not a veggie ______

4. tenpins ______

5. it's a kick ______

Answers

Page 33
1. Twain, Mark
2. Beatrix, Potter
3. Milne, A.A
4. Seuss, Dr.
5. White, E.B.

Page 34
1. hospital
2. museum
3. school
4. library
5. hotel

Page 35
1. France
2. China
3. Australia
4. Spain
5. England

Page 36
1. greyhound
2. pointer
3. beagle
4. boxer
5. husky

Page 37
1. habitat
2. ecology
3. botany
4. meteorology
5. oxygen

Page 38
1. cow
2. pig
3. horse
4. sheep
5. chicken

Page 39
1. Monopoly
2. Trivial Pursuit
3. Chess
4. Scrabble
5. Cluedo

Page 40
1. desert
2. grasslands
3. rainforests
4. oceans
5. swamps

Page 41
1. termite
2. ant
3. mosquito
4. firefly
5. ladybird

Page 42
1. Three days old.
2. It gets unhoppy.
3. She wanted rich soil.
4. Palm.
5. A bedbug.

Page 43
1. skull
2. jaw
3. collarbone
4. elbow
5. pelvis
6. kneecap
7. shin
8. ankle

Page 44

	Patti	Mary	Paul
Pizza	**no**		
Spaghetti	**yes**		
Chicken	**no**		

	Patti	Mary	Paul
Pizza	**no**	**no**	
Spaghetti	**yes**	**no**	
Chicken	**no**	**yes**	

	Patti	Mary	Paul
Pizza	**no**	**no**	**yes**
Spaghetti	**yes**	**no**	**no**
Chicken	**no**	**yes**	**no**

spaghetti
chicken
pizza

Page 45
1. giraffe
2. elephant
3. whale
4. bat
5. fox

Page 46

A. 2	2				B. 1	0	5
9		C. 2	9		9		
6		2				D. 1	7
	E. 1	2				5	
F. 1	2		G. 1	0	5		
8			5			H. 2	8
	I. 8	5				3	
	5				J. 1	6	

Page 47
1. Arctic Ocean
2. Antarctic Ocean
3. Pacific Ocean
4. Pacific Ocean
5. Indian Ocean
6. Atlantic Ocean

Page 48
1. Mahatma Gandhi
2. Mother Teresa
3. Nelson Mandela
4. Martin Luther King
5. Dalai Lama

Page 49
1. feather
2. night
3. nails
4. bird
5. silk

Page 50
1. Africa
2. South America
3. Asia
4. North America

Page 51
1. galaxy
2. light and heat
3. gas
4. Milky Way
5. energy

Page 52
1. rug
2. computer
3. pound
4. author
5. brake

Page 53
1. United Kingdom
2. Uruguay
3. United States
4. United Arab Emirates
5. Ukraine

Page 54
flower/broccoli
cauliflower
stem/celery
asparagus
leaf/lettuce
spinach
seed/pea
bean
root/sweet potato
carrot

Page 55
1. tornado
2. snowstorm
3. rainbow
4. hurricane
5. thunderstorm

Page 56
1. Branson
2. Joplin
3. St. Louis
4. Kansas City
5. Hannibal
6. Sedalia

Page 57
1. glaciers
2. Louisiana Purchase
3. Wyoming
4. geyser
5. oldest

Page 58
1. cheetah
2. ostrich
3. flea
4. chameleon
5. platypus

Page 59
1. currents
2. salt
3. tide
4. waves
5. sand

Page 60
1. not understood
2. happy
3. be quiet
4. get angry
5. tell a secret

Page 61
1. dinosaurs
2. tongue
3. iguana
4. slugs
5. tails

Page 62
1. precipitation
2. condensation
3. air pressure
4. water
5. wind

Page 63
1. tennis
2. golf
3. squash
4. bowling
5. football